Sole trader and partnership accounts (AP2)

Workbook

David Cox

**osborne
BOOKS**

Published by Osborne Books Limited
Unit 1B Everoak Estate
Bromyard Road
Worcester WR2 5HP
Tel 01905 748071
Email books@osbornebooks.co.uk
Website www.osbornebooks.co.uk

Design by Laura Ingham
Cover and page design image © Istockphoto.com/Petrovich9

Printed and bound by CPI Group (UK) Ltd, Croydon, CR0 4YY

British Library Cataloguing in Publication Data
A catalogue record for this book is available from the British Library

ISBN 978 1905777 761

Contents

		questions	answers

Chapter activities and answers

Accounts Preparation 2

Practice assessments and answers

Acknowledgements

The publisher wishes to thank the following for their help with the reading and production of the book: Jean Cox, Maz Loton and Cathy Turner. Thanks are also due to Roger Petheram for his technical editorial work and to Laura Ingham for her designs for this series.

The publisher is indebted to the Association of Accounting Technicians for its kind permission for the reproduction of its sample assessment in this text.

Author

David Cox has more than twenty years' experience teaching accountancy students over a wide range of levels. Formerly with the Management and Professional Studies Department at Worcester College of Technology, he now lectures on a freelance basis and carries out educational consultancy work in accountancy studies. He is author and joint author of a number of textbooks in the areas of accounting, finance and banking.

Introduction

what this book covers

This book has been written specifically to cover the Learning Area 'Accounts Preparation II' which combine two QCF Units in the AAT Level 3 Diploma in Accounting:

- Prepare accounts for partnerships
- Prepare final accounts for sole traders

what this book contains

This book is set out in two sections:

- **Chapter activities** which provide extra practice material in addition to the activities included in the Osborne Books Tutorial text. Answers to the Chapter activities are set out in this book.

- **Practice assessments** are included to prepare the student for the Computer Based Assessment. They are based directly on the structure, style and content of the sample assessment materials provided by the AAT at www.aat.org.uk. Suggested answers to the Practice Assessments are set out in this book.

online support from Osborne Books

This book is supported by practice material available at www.osbornebooks.co.uk

This material is available to tutors – and to students at their discretion – in two forms:

- A **Tutor Zone** which is available to tutors who have adopted the Osborne Books texts. This area of the website provides extra assessment practice material (plus answers) in addition to the activities included in this Workbook text.

- **Online learning** – online practice questions designed to familiarise students with the style of the AAT Computer Based Assessments.

  Scan the code on the right using your Smartphone to gain access to the online practice questions.

further information

If you want to know more about our products, please visit www.osbornebooks.co.uk, email books@osbornebooks.co.uk or telephone Osborne Books Customer Services on 01905 748071.

Chapter activities

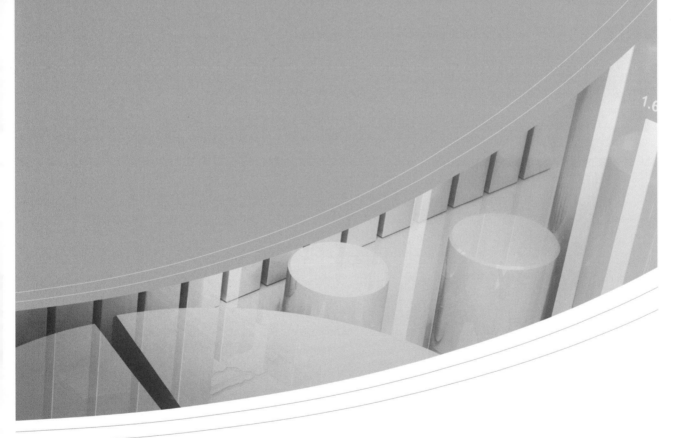

12 Chapter activities
Sole trader financial statements

12.1 Cost of sales is calcuated as:

	✔
opening inventory + purchases − closing inventory	
purchases − opening inventory + closing inventory	
opening inventory + purchases + closing inventory	
purchases − opening inventory − closing inventory	

12.2 Which one of the following is used to calculate profit for the year?

	✔
two-column trial balance	
sales ledger	
statement of financial position	
income statement	

12.3 Which one of the following describes net current assets?

	✔
the excess of non-current assets over non-current (long-term) liabilities	
the excess of current assets over non-current (long-term) liabilities	
the excess of current assets over current liabilities	
the excess of non-current assets over current liabilities	

12.4 You are to fill in the missing figures for the following sole trader businesses:

	Sales	Opening inventory	Purchases	Closing inventory	Gross profit	Expenses	Profit/loss* for year
	£	£	£	£	£	£	£
Business A	20,000	5,000	10,000	3,000	....	4,000	....
Business B	35,000	8,000	15,000	5,000	....	....	10,000
Business C	....	6,500	18,750	7,250	18,500	11,750	....
Business D	45,250	9,500	....	10,500	20,750	....	10,950
Business E	71,250	....	49,250	9,100	22,750	24,450	....
Business F	25,650	4,950	13,750	....	11,550	....	(3,450)

* Note: a loss is indicated by brackets

12.5 This Activity is about calculating missing balances and the accounting equation.

You are given the following information about a sole trader as at 1 April 20-4:

The value of assets and liabilities was:

- Non-current assets at carrying amount £35,400
- Inventory £12,200
- Trade receivables £21,650
- Bank (overdrawn) £3,240
- Trade payables £12,790

There were no other assets or liabilities.

(a) **Calculate the capital account balance as at 1 April 20-4.**

£

(b) **On 30 April 20-4, a new machine is purchased for use in the business and is paid for immediately by bank payment. Tick the boxes to show what effect this transaction will have on the balances. You must choose ONE answer for EACH line.**

	Debit ✓	Credit ✓	No change ✓
Non-current assets			
Trade receivables			
Trade payables			
Bank			
Capital			

(c) **Which of the following is best described as a non-current (long-term) liability? Tick ONE answer.**

	✓
A bank loan repayable in two years' time	
A bank overdraft	
Trade payables	
Trade receivables	

12.6   The following trial balance has been extracted by Matt Smith at 31 December 20-4:

	Dr £	Cr £
Opening inventory	14,350	
Purchases	114,472	
Sales revenue		259,688
Rent and rates	13,718	
Heating and lighting	12,540	
Wages and salaries	42,614	
Vehicle expenses	5,817	
Advertising	6,341	
Premises at cost	75,000	
Office equipment at cost	33,000	
Vehicles at cost	21,500	
Sales ledger control	23,854	
Bank	1,235	
Cash	125	
Capital		62,500
Drawings	12,358	
Loan from bank		35,000
Purchases ledger control		14,258
Value Added Tax		5,478
Closing inventory: income statement		16,280
Closing inventory: statement of financial position	16,280	
	393,204	393,204

You are to prepare the financial statements of Matt Smith for the year ended 31 December 20-4, using the conventional format.

12.7 An extract from the trial balance of Lisa James is as follows:

Trial balance (extract) as at 31 March 20-7

	Dr	Cr
	£	£
Opening inventory	17,540 ✓	
Sales revenue		127,500 ✓
Purchases	77,200 ✓	
Sales returns	2,150 ✓	
Purchases returns		3,040 ✓
Carriage in	680 ✓	
Carriage out	1,540 ✓	
Discount received		230 ✓
Discount allowed	470	
Other expenses	35,830	
Closing inventory: income statement		19,960

Handwritten margin notes: Purch (beside Carriage in); Exp. (beside Carriage out); Inc. (beside Discount received); Exp. (beside Discount allowed)

You are to prepare the income statement of Lisa James for the year ended 31 March 20-7, using the conventional format.

Chapter activities

13 Adjustments to sole trader financial statements

13.1 An income statement shows a profit for the year of £14,900. It is discovered that no allowance has been made for advertising expenses accrued of £620 and rent prepaid of £450 at the year end. What is the adjusted profit for the year?

	✔
£14,730	
£15,070	
£15,970	
£13,830	

13.2 Identify whether the following items will be stated in the year end income statement as income or expense by putting a tick in the relevant column of the table below.

Item	Income ✔	Expense ✔
Profit on disposal of non-current asset		
Decrease in allowance for doubtful debts		
Irrecoverable debts		
Discount allowed		
Depreciation charge		
Commission received		

13.3 An income statement shows a profit for the year of £18,790. The owner of the business wishes to increase the allowance for doubtful debts by £800 and to write off irrecoverable debts of £250. What is the adjusted profit for the year?

	✔
£18,240	
£19,840	
£19,340	
£17,740	

13.4   You have the following trial balance for a sole trader known as Tysoe Trading. All the necessary year end adjustments have been made.

(a)   **Prepare an income statement (on the next page) for the business for the year ended 31 March 20-6.**

Tysoe Trading Trial balance as at 31 March 20-6		
	Dr £	Cr £
Accruals		460
Bank	4,610	
Capital		35,500
Closing inventory	10,200	10,200
Depreciation charge	2,500	
Discounts allowed	490	
Drawings	10,300	
General expenses	25,720	
Office equipment at cost	20,400	
Office equipment: accumulated depreciation		6,500
Opening inventory	11,450	
Prepayments	990	
Purchases	64,330	
Purchases ledger control		10,310
Rent and rates	7,240	
Sales revenue		140,680
Sales ledger control	18,920	
Value Added Tax		3,110
Wages	29,610	
	206,760	206,760

Tysoe Trading Income statement for the year ended 31 March 20-6		
	£	£
Sales revenue		
Cost of sales		
Gross profit		
Less expenses:		
Total expenses		
Profit for the year		

(b) Indicate where accruals of expenses should be shown in the statement of financial position. Tick ONE from:

	✓
As a non-current asset	
As a current asset	
As a current liability	
As an addition to capital	

(c) State the meaning of a credit balance for disposal of a non-current asset in a trial balance. Tick ONE from:

	✓
The business has made a profit on disposal	
The business has made a loss on disposal	
The asset has been under depreciated	
The asset has been part-exchanged on disposal	

13.5 The following adjusted trial balance has been taken from the books of Rhianna Aitken, who sells kitchenware, as at 31 March 20-1:

	Dr £	Cr £
Sales ledger control	4,110	
Allowance for doubtful debts		880
Allowance for doubtful debts: adjustment	220	
Purchases ledger control		11,490
Value Added Tax		1,720
Bank		2,360
Capital		27,500
Sales revenue		166,240
Purchases	85,330	
Opening inventory	18,890	
Shop wages	35,560	
Prepayment of shop wages	440	
Heat and light	2,680	
Rent and rates	10,570	
Accrual of rent and rates		590
Shop fittings at cost	36,000	
Shop fittings: depreciation charge	4,750	
Shop fittings: accumulated depreciation		12,380
Disposal of non-current asset		600
Irrecoverable debts	150	
Drawings	25,060	
Closing inventory	22,450	22,450
	246,210	246,210

You are to prepare the financial statements of Rhianna Aitken for the year ended 31 March 20-1, using the conventional format.

14 Chapter activities
Incomplete records

14.1 · Cost of sales for the year is £250,000.
· Mark-up is 50%.

What is sales revenue for the year?

	✔
£375,000	
£125,000	
£250,000	
£500,000	

14.2 · Sales for the year are £200,000.
· Margin is 30%.
· Opening inventory is £15,000; closing inventory is £20,000.

What are purchases for the year?

	✔
£260,000	
£160,000	
£140,000	
£145,000	

14.3 You are preparing accounts from incomplete records. Trade payables at the start of the year were £16,400. During the year purchases on credit total £73,400, bank payments to payables total £68,100, purchases returns total £1,800, and discounts received total £400.

What is the trade payables figure at the end of the year?

	✔
£13,300	
£20,300	
£19,500	
£23,900	

14.4   Talib Zabbar owns a shop selling children's clothes. He is convinced that one of his employees is stealing goods from the shop. He asks you to calculate from the accounting records the value of inventory stolen. The following information is available for the year ended 31 March 20-2:

* sales for the year, £160,000

* opening inventory at the beginning of the year, £30,500

* purchases for the year, £89,500

* closing inventory at the end of the year, £21,500

* the gross profit margin achieved on all sales is 40 per cent

You are to calculate the value of inventory stolen (if any) during the year ended 31 March 20-2.

14.5   This Activity is about finding missing figures in ledger accounts where the records are incomplete.

You are working on the financial statements of a business for the year ended 31 March 20-8. You have the following information.

Day book summaries for the year	Net £	VAT £	Total £
Sales	102,000	20,400	122,400
Purchases	64,000	12,800	76,800
Sales returns	1,800	360	2,160
Purchases returns	1,240	248	1,488

All sales and purchases are on credit terms

Balances as at:	31 March 20-7 £	31 March 20-8 £
Trade receivables	16,250	18,110
Trade payables	10,380	not known

Further information:	Net £	VAT £	Total £
Administration expenses	22,000	4,400	26,400

Administration expenses are not included in the purchases figure in purchases day book

Bank summary	Dr £		Cr £
Balance b/d	10,680	Travel expenses	5,290
Trade receivables	117,950	Administration expenses	26,400
Balance c/d	6,313	Trade payables	72,833
		HMRC for VAT	2,760
		Drawings	10,500
		Wages	17,160
	134,943		134,943

There were no settlement (cash) discounts on payments made to trade payables.

(a) Using the figures given on the previous page, prepare the sales ledger control account for the year ended 31 March 20-8. Show clearly settlement (cash) discounts as the balancing figure.

Sales ledger control account

(b) Using the figures given on the previous page, prepare the purchases ledger control account for the year ended 31 March 20-8. Show clearly the trade payables figure at the end of the year as the balancing figure.

Purchases ledger control account

(c) Find the closing balance for VAT by preparing the VAT control account for the year ended 31 March 20-8. Use the figures given on the previous page.

Note: The business is not charged VAT on its travel expenses.

VAT control account

		Balance b/d	1,470

15 Chapter activities
Partnership financial statements

15.1 A partnership may choose to over-ride some or all of the accounting rules in the Partnership Act 1890 by the partners entering into a separate:

	✔
appropriation account	
accounting policy	
partnership agreement	
loan agreement	

15.2 Profits of a two-person partnership are £32,100 before the following are taken into account:

- interest on partners' capital accounts, £1,800
- salary of one partner, £10,000
- interest on partners' drawings £700

If the remaining profits are shared equally, how much will each partner receive?

	✔
£10,500	
£11,400	
£12,300	
£16,400	

15.3 You have the following information about a partnership business:

- The financial year ends on 31 March

- The partners are Uma, Val and Win

- Partners' annual salaries:
  - Uma   £10,400
  - Val   £15,200
  - Win   £16,750

- Partners' capital account balances as at 31 March 20-4:
  - Uma   £20,000
  - Val   £35,000
  - Win   £15,000

  Interest on capital is allowed at 4% per annum on the capital account balance at the end of the financial year.

- Interest charged on partners' drawings:
  - Uma   £240
  - Val   £360
  - Win   £290

- The partners share the remaining profit of £18,000 as follows:
  - Uma   30%
  - Val   50%
  - Win   20%

- Partners' drawings for the year:
  - Uma   £14,400
  - Val   £23,600
  - Win   £18,200

Prepare the current accounts for the partners for the year ended 31 March 20-4. Show clearly the balances carried down. You MUST enter zeros where appropriate in order to obtain full mark. Do NOT use brackets, minus signs or dashes.

Current accounts

	Uma £	Val £	Win £		Uma £	Val £	Win £
Balance b/d	0	0	300	Balance b/d	1,200	700	0

15.4   This Activity is about preparing a partnership statement of financial position.

You are preparing the statement of financial position for the RS Partnership for the year ended 31 March 20-3. The partners are Ros and Sam.

All the necessary year end adjustments have been made, except for the transfer of profit to the current accounts of the partners.

Before sharing profits the balances of the partners' current accounts are:

- Ros   £500 credit

- Sam   £250 debit

Each partner is entitled to £5,500 profit share.

(a)   **Calculate the balance of each partner's current account after sharing profits. Fill in the answers below.**

Current account balance: Ros	£
Current account balance: Sam	£

Note: these balances will need to be transferred into the statement of financial position of the partnership which follows.

You have the following trial balance. All the necessary year end adjustments have been made.

(b) **Prepare a statement of financial position for the partnership as at 31 March 20-3. You need to use the partners' current account balances that you have just calculated. Do NOT use brackets, minus signs or dashes.**

RS Partnership
Trial balance as at 31 March 20-3

	Dr £	Cr £
Accruals		230
Administration expenses	22,680	
Allowance for doubtful debts		670
Allowance for doubtful debts: adjustment		120
Bank	8,910	
Capital account – Ros		30,000
Capital account – Sam		25,000
Cash	490	
Closing inventory	11,670	11,670
Current account – Ros		500
Current account – Sam	250	
Depreciation charge	2,500	
Disposal of non-current asset		300
Office equipment at cost	32,000	
Office equipment: accumulated depreciation		7,900
Opening inventory	10,430	
Purchases	90,850	
Purchases ledger control		13,370
Rent and rates	5,280	
Sales revenue		130,650
Sales ledger control	37,310	
Value Added Tax		1,960
Total	222,370	222,370

RS Partnership

Statement of financial position as at 31 March 20-3

	Cost	Accumulated depreciation	Carrying amount (net book value)
Non-current (fixed) assets	£	£	£
Current assets			
Current liabilities			
Net current assets			
Net assets			
Financed by:	Ros	Sam	Total.

16 Chapter activities
Changes in partnerships

16.1 Mia, Nell and Olly are in partnership sharing profits equally. Mia is to retire and it is agreed that goodwill is worth £30,000. After Mia's retirement, Nell and Olly will continue to run the partnership and will share profits equally. What will be the goodwill adjustments to Nell's capital account?

	✔
debit £10,000; credit £10,000	
debit £10,000; credit £15,000	
debit £15,000; credit £15,000	
debit £15,000; credit £10,000	

16.2 Norman and Oliver are in partnership sharing profits equally. Each has a capital account with a balance of £75,000. Peter joins as a new partner. The profit share will be Norman 40%, Oliver 40% and Peter 20%. An adjustment is made for goodwill on the admission of Peter to the value of £40,000, but no goodwill is to be left in the accounts. What will be the balance of Oliver's capital account after the creation and elimination of goodwill?

	✔
£71,000	
£79,000	
£91,000	
£95,000	

16.3   You have the following information about a partnership:

The partners are Sue and Tom.

- Uma was admitted to the partnership on 1 April 20-3 when she paid £25,000 into the bank account as her capital.

- Profit share, effective until 31 March 20-3:
    - Sue   60%
    - Tom   40%

- Profit share, effective from 1 April 20-3:
    - Sue   50%
    - Tom   30%
    - Uma   20%

- Goodwill was valued at £30,000 on 31 March 20-3.

- Goodwill is to be introduced into the partners' capital accounts on 31 March and then eliminated on 1 April.

(a)   **Prepare the goodwill account of the partnership, showing clearly the transactions on the admission of Uma, the new partner.**

Goodwill account

(b)   **Prepare the capital account for Uma, the new partner, showing clearly the balance carried down as at 1 April 20-3.**

Capital account – Uma

		Balance b/d	0

(c) **Identify whether the following statements about the partnership of Sue, Tom and Uma are true or false by putting a tick in the relevant column of the table below.**

Statement	True ✔	False ✔
Sue and Tom have each paid money to Uma when she joined the partnership.		
The goodwill of £30,000 is kept in a separate bank account, in accordance with the requirements of the Partnership Act 1890.		
Uma has paid a premium for a 20% share of the profits of the partnership.		
With goodwill valued at £30,000, Sue and Tom will each have £15,000 extra profit this year.		

16.4   You have the following information about a partnership business:

- The financial year ends on 31 March.

- The partners at the beginning of the year were Jim and Kit.

- Leo was admitted to the partnership on 1 January 20-5.

- There is no interest on partners' capital.

- Partners' annual salaries:

    - Jim   £20,000

    - Kit   £18,000

    - Leo   £10,000

- Partners' interest on drawings:

    - Jim   £500 per full year

    - Kit   £300 per full year

    - Leo   £200 per full year

- Profit share, effective until 31 December 20-4:

    - Jim   60%

    - Kit   40%

- Profit share, effective from 1 January 20-5:

    - Jim   50%

    - Kit   30%

    - Leo   20%

Profit for the year ended 31 March 20-5 was £64,000. You can assume that profits accrued evenly during the year.

Prepare the appropriation account (on the next page) for the partnership for the year ended 31 March 20-5.

Partnership Appropriation account for the year ended 31 March 20-5

	1 Apr 20-4 – 31 Dec 20-4 £	1 Jan 20-5 – 31 Mar 20-5 £	Total £
Profit			
Salaries:			
Jim			
Kit			
Leo			
Interest on drawings:			
Jim			
Kit			
Leo			
Profit available for distribution			

Profit share			
Jim			
Kit			
Leo			
Total profit distributed			

Answers to chapter activities

12 Chapter activities – answers
Sole trader financial statements

12.1 opening inventory + purchases – closing inventory

12.2 income statement

12.3 the excess of current assets over current liabilities

12.4 Business A: gross profit £8,000, profit for year £4,000

Business B: gross profit £17,000, expenses £7,000

Business C: sales £36,500, profit for year £6,750

Business D: purchases £25,500, expenses £9,800

Business E: opening inventory £8,350, loss for year £1,700

Business F: closing inventory £4,600, expenses £15,000

12.5

(a)

£53,220

(b)

	Debit ✓	Credit ✓	No change ✓
Non-current assets	✓		
Trade receivables			✓
Trade payables			✓
Bank		✓	
Capital			✓

(c)

A bank loan repayable in two years' time	✓

12.6

MATT SMITH

INCOME STATEMENT
for the year ended 31 December 20-4

	£	£
Sales revenue		259,688
Opening inventory	14,350	
Purchases	114,472	
	128,822	
Less Closing inventory	16,280	
Cost of sales		112,542
Gross profit		147,146
Less expenses:		
Rent and rates	13,718	
Heating and lighting	12,540	
Wages and salaries	42,614	
Vehicle expenses	5,817	
Advertising	6,341	
		81,030
Profit for the year		66,116

STATEMENT OF FINANCIAL POSITION as at 31 December 20-4

	£	£	£
Non-current assets			
Premises at cost			75,000
Office equipment at cost			33,000
Vehicles at cost			21,500
			129,500
Current assets			
Inventory (closing)		16,280	
Receivables		23,854	
Bank		1,235	
Cash		125	
		41,494	
Less Current liabilities			
Payables	14,258		
Value Added Tax	5,478		
		19,736	
Net current assets			21,758
			151,258
Less Non-current liabilities			
Loan from bank			35,000
NET ASSETS			116,258
FINANCED BY			
Capital			
Opening capital			62,500
Add Profit for the year			66,116
			128,616
Less Drawings			12,358
Closing capital			116,258

12.7

LISA JAMES
INCOME STATEMENT
for the year ended 31 March 20-7

	£	£	£
Sales revenue			127,500
Less Sales returns			2,150
Net sales revenue			125,350
Opening inventory		17,540	
Purchases	77,200		
Add Carriage in	680		
	77,880		
Less Purchases returns	3,040		
Net purchases		74,840	
		92,380	
Less Closing inventory		19,960	
Cost of sales			72,420
Gross profit			52,930
Add income: Discount received			230
			53,160
Less expenses:			
Discount allowed		470	
Carriage out		1,540	
Other expenses		35,830	
			37,840
Profit for the year			15,320

13 Chapter activities – answers
Adjustments to sole trader financial statements

13.1 £14,730

13.2

Item	Income ✔	Expense ✔
Profit on disposal of non-current asset	✔	
Decrease in allowance for doubtful debts	✔	
Irrecoverable debts		✔
Discount allowed		✔
Depreciation charge		✔
Commission received	✔	

13.3 £17,740

13.4 **(a)**

Tysoe Trading Income statement for the year ended 31 March 20-6		
	£	£
Sales revenue		140,680
Opening inventory	11,450	
Purchases	64,330	
Closing inventory	(10,200)	
Cost of sales		65,580
Gross profit		75,100
Less expenses:		
Depreciation charge	2,500	
Discounts allowed	490	
General expenses	25,720	
Rent and rates	7,240	
Wages	29,610	
Total expenses		65,560
Profit for the year		9,540

(b)

As a current liability	✓

(c)

The business has made a profit on disposal	✓

13.5

RHIANNA AITKEN
INCOME STATEMENT
for the year ended 31 March 20-1

	£	£
Sales revenue		166,240
Opening inventory	18,890	
Purchases	85,330	
	104,220	
Less Closing inventory	22,450	
Cost of sales		81,770
Gross profit		84,470
Add income:		
Profit on disposal of non-current asset		600
		85,070
Less expenses:		
Allowance for doubtful debts: adjustment	220	
Shop wages	35,560	
Heat and light	2,680	
Rent and rates	10,570	
Depreciation charge: shop fittings	4,750	
Irrecoverable debts	150	
		53,930
Profit for the year		31,140

STATEMENT OF FINANCIAL POSITION
as at 31 March 20-1

	£ Cost	£ Accumulated depreciation	£ Carrying amount
Non-current assets			
Shop fittings	36,000	12,380	23,620
Current assets			
Inventory		22,450	
Trade receivables	4,110		
Less allowance for doubtful debts	880		
		3,230	
Prepayment of expenses		440	
		26,120	
Less Current liabilities			
Trade payables	11,490		
Accrual of expenses	590		
Value Added Tax	1,720		
Bank	2,360		
		16,160	
Net current assets			9,960
NET ASSETS			33,580
FINANCED BY			
Capital			
Opening capital			27,500
Add Profit for the year			31,140
			58,640
Less Drawings			25,060
Closing capital			33,580

14

Chapter activities – answers
Incomplete records

14.1   £375,000

Workings: £250,000 + £125,000 profit

14.2   £145,000

Workings: cost of sales = £140,000 + closing inventory £20,000 = £160,000 – opening inventory £15,000

14.3   £19,500

Workings: £16,400 + £73,400 – £68,100 – £1,800 – £400

14.4

TALIB ZABBAR
CALCULATION OF INVENTORY LOSS FOR THE YEAR ENDED 31 MARCH 20-2

	£	£
Opening inventory		30,500
Purchases		89,500
Cost of inventory available for sale		120,000
Sales	160,000	
Less Normal gross profit margin (40%)	64,000	
Cost of sales		96,000
Estimated closing inventory		24,000
Less Actual closing inventory		21,500
Value of inventory loss		2,500

14.5 (a) Sales ledger control account

Balance b/d	16,250	Sales returns day book	2,160
Sales day book	122,400	Bank	117,950
		Discounts allowed	430
		Balance c/d	18,110
	138,650		138,650

(b) Purchases ledger control account

Purchases returns day book	1,488	Balance b/d	10,380
Bank	72,833	Purchases day book	76,800
Balance c/d	12,859		
	87,180		87,180

(c) VAT control account

Purchases day book	12,800	Balance b/d	1,470
Sales returns day book	360	Sales day book	20,400
Administration expenses	4,400	Purchases returns day book	248
Bank	2,760		
Balance c/d	1,798		
	22,118		22,118

15

Chapter activities – answers
Partnership financial statements

15.1 partnership agreement

15.2 £10,500

15.3

Current accounts

	Uma £	Val £	Win £		Uma £	Val £	Win £
Balance b/d	0	0	300	Balance b/d	1,200	700	0
Drawings	14,400	23,600	18,200	Salaries	10,400	15,200	16,750
Interest on drawings	240	360	290	Interest on capital	800	1,400	600
Balance c/d	3,160	2,340	2,160	Profit share	5,400	9,000	3,600
	17,800	26,300	20,950		17,800	26,300	20,950

15.4 **(a)**

Current account balance: Ros	£6,000
Current account balance: Sam	£5,250

(b)   **RS Partnership**
Statement of financial position as at 31 March 20-3

	Cost	Accumulated depreciation	Carrying amount (net book value)
Non-current (fixed) assets	£	£	£
Office equipment	32,000	7,900	24,100
Current assets			
Inventory		11,670	
Trade receivables		*36,640	
Bank		8,910	
Cash		490	
		57,710	
Current liabilities			
Trade payables	13,370		
Value Added Tax	1,960		
Accruals	230		
		15,560	
Net current assets			42,150
Net assets			66,250

Financed by:	Ros	Sam	Total
Capital accounts	30,000	25,000	55,000
Current accounts	6,000	5,250	11,250
	36,000	30,250	66,250

* sales ledger control £37,310 *minus* allowance for doubtful debts £670
= trade receivables £36,640

16 Chapter activities – answers
Changes in partnerships

16.1 debit £15,000; credit £10,000

16.2 £79,000

Workings: £75,000 + (£40,000 x 50%) − (£40,000 x 40%)

16.3 (a)   Goodwill account

Capital – Sue	18,000	Capital – Sue	15,000
Capital – Tom	12,000	Capital – Tom	9,000
		Capital – Uma	6,000
	30,000		30,000

(b)   Capital account – Uma

Goodwill	6,000	Balance b/d	0
Balance c/d	19,000	Bank	25,000
	25,000		25,000

(c)

Statement	True ✔	False ✔
Sue and Tom have each paid money to Uma when she joined the partnership.		✔
The goodwill of £30,000 is kept in a separate bank account, in accordance with the requirements of the Partnership Act 1890.		✔
Uma has paid a premium for a 20% share of the profits of the partnership.	✔	
With goodwill valued at £30,000, Sue and Tom will each have £15,000 extra profit this year.		✔

16.4

Partnership Appropriation account for the year ended 31 March 20-5

	1 Apr 20-4 – 31 Dec 20-4 £	1 Jan 20-5 – 31 Mar 20-5 £	Total £
Profit	48,000	16,000	64,000
Salaries:			
Jim	15,000	5,000	20,000
Kit	13,500	4,500	18,000
Leo	0	2,500	2,500
Interest on drawings:			
Jim	375	125	500
Kit	225	75	300
Leo	0	50	50
Profit available for distribution	20,100	4,250	24,350

Profit share			
Jim	12,060	2,125	14,185
Kit	8,040	1,275	9,315
Leo	0	850	850
Total profit distributed	20,100	4,250	24,350

Accounts preparation 2

Practice assessment 1

Time allowance: 2 hours

- Each task of the Assessment is to be answered separately.
- The rate of Value Added Tax used is 20%.

Section 1: Incomplete records

Task 1.1

This task is about finding missing figures in ledger accounts where the records are incomplete.

You are working on the financial statements of a business for the year ended 31 March 20X1. You have the following information.

Day book summaries for the year	Net £	VAT £	Total £
Sales	134,000	26,800	160,800
Sales returns	2,400	480	2,880
Purchases	82,000	16,400	98,400
Purchases returns	1,600	320	1,920

Note: all sales and purchases are on credit terms

Further information	Net £	VAT £	Total £
Office expenses	20,600	4,120	24,720

Note: office expenses are not included in the purchases day book

Bank summary	Dr £		Cr £
Balance b/d	10,770	Office expenses	24,720
Trade receivables	152,490	Trade payables	92,845
Balance c/d	3,400	HMRC for VAT	5,245
		Drawings	17,500
		Wages	26,350
	166,660		166,660

Further information:
- Cash (settlement) discounts received during the year were £550.
- Cash (settlement) discounts allowed during the year were £230.

(a) **Using the figures given on the previous page, prepare the sales ledger control account for the year ended 31 March 20X1. Show clearly the amount of trade receivables at the year end as the balance carried down.**

Sales ledger control account

Balance b/d	18,275		

(b) **Using the figures given on the previous page, prepare the purchases ledger control account for the year ended 31 March 20X1. Show clearly the amount of trade payables at the year end as the balance carried down.**

Purchases ledger control account

		Balance b/d	10,365

(c)   Using the figures given on page 162, prepare the VAT control account for the year ended 31 March 20X1. Show clearly the amount of VAT due to HM Revenue and Customs at the year end as the balance carried down.

VAT control account

		Balance b/d	2,140

Task 1.2

This task is about calculating missing balances and the accounting equation.

You are given the following information about a sole trader business as at 1 April 20X1:The value of assets and liabilities were:

•	Inventory	£14,270
•	Bank (overdrawn)	£3,210
•	Trade payables	£6,180
•	Non-current assets at carrying amount	£25,500
•	Bank loan	£12,500
•	Trade receivables	£9,450

There were no other assets or liabilities.

(a) Calculate the capital account balance as at 1 April 20X1.

£

For the year ended 31 March 20X1 you have the following information:

•	Trade payables at 1 April 20X0	£7,240
•	Trade payables at 31 March 20X1	£6,180
•	Bank payments to trade payables during the year	£51,420
•	Cash purchases during the year	£1,730

(b) Calculate the purchases for the year ended 31 March 20X1.

£

(c) **Which of the following best describes goodwill? Tick ONE answer.**

	✔
A liability, where payment is due in more than one year's time.	
An intangible non-current asset which does not have material substance.	
A short-term asset which changes regularly.	
A tangible non-current asset which has material substance.	

Section 2: Final accounts

Task 2.1

This task is about preparing the financial statements (final accounts) for sole traders.

You have the following trial balance for a sole trader known as Tairo Trading. All the necessary year end adjustments have been made.

(a) **Prepare an income statement (on the next page) for the business for the year ended 31 March 20X1.**

Tairo Trading Trial balance as at 31 March 20X1	Dr £	Cr £
Accruals		540
Bank		1,470
Capital		30,180
Closing inventory	8,350	8,350
Depreciation charge	6,240	
Discounts allowed	350	
Drawings	11,970	
General expenses	13,860	
Opening inventory	6,290	
Prepayments	330	
Purchases	93,760	
Purchases ledger control		10,850
Rent and rates	10,390	
Sales revenue		160,830
Sales ledger control	22,820	
Value Added Tax		5,640
Vehicles at cost	25,300	
Vehicles: accumulated depreciation		10,250
Wages	28,450	
	228,110	228,110

Handwritten annotations in left margin:
SFP, SFP, SFP, BoL, IS, IS, SCP, IS, IS SFP, SFP, IS, SCP, IS, IS, SCP, SFP, SFP, SFP, IS

Tairo Trading Income statement for the year ended 31 March 20X1		
	£	£
Sales revenue		
Cost of sales		
Gross profit		
Less expenses:		
Total expenses		
Profit for the year		

(b) Indicate where prepayments of expenses should be shown in the statement of financial position. Tick ONE from:

	✓
As a non-current asset	
As a current asset	
As a current liability	
As a non-current (long-term) liability	

(c)   Each of the four statements, below, describes an objective that makes financial information useful. The objectives are comparability, ease of understanding, relevance and reliability.

Match the objective to the statement.

Statement	Objective
Financial information that is useful to users of the financial statements.	
Financial information that can be depended upon by users.	
Financial statements that can be compared with those from previous years.	
Users of financial statements can understand the information given.	

Task 2.2

This task is about accounting for partnerships.

You have the following information about a partnership:

The partners are Kay, Lee and Matt.

- Kay is to retire from the partnership on 1 April 20X1. Lee and Matt will continue in partnership. Kay agrees to leave £25,000 of the amount due to her as a loan to the new partnership; the remainder will be paid to her from the partnership bank account.

- Profit share, effective until 31 March 20X1:
    - Kay   40%
    - Lee   40%
    - Matt   20%

- Profit share, effective from 1 April 20X1:
    - Lee   50%
    - Matt   50%

- Goodwill was valued at £30,000 on 31 March 20X1.

- Goodwill is to be introduced into the partners' capital accounts on 31 March and then eliminated on 1 April

- Current accounts are not used by the partnership.

(a)   **Prepare the capital account for Kay, the partner who is retiring, showing clearly the amount to be paid to her from the partnership bank account as at 1 April 20X1.**

Capital account – Kay

	£		£
		Balance b/d	48,500

(b) **Identify whether the following statements about a partnership agreement are true or false by putting a tick in the relevant column of the table below.**

Statement	True ✔	False ✔
All partnership agreements state that profits and losses must be shared equally between the partners.		
A partnership agreement will state the salaries to be paid to employees.		
A partnership agreement may state that interest is to be allowed on partners' capitals, and at what rate.		
A partnership agreement may state that interest is to be charged on partners' drawings, and at what rate.		

Task 2.3

This task is about partnership accounts.

You have the following information about a partnership business:

- The financial year ends on 31 March.

- The partners at the beginning of the year were Jane and Kate.

- Lysa was admitted to the partnership on 1 July 20X0.

- Partners' annual salaries:

  - Jane   £20,000

  - Kate   £24,000

  - Lysa   nil

- Partners' interest on capital:

  - Jane   £1,200 per full year

  - Kate   £1,800 per full year

  - Lysa   £400 per full year

- Profit share, effective until 30 June 20X0:

  - Jane   60%

  - Kate   40%

- Profit share, effective from 1 July 20X0:

  - Jane   50%

  - Kate   30%

  - Lysa   20%

Profit for the year ended 31 March 20X1 was £68,000. You can assume that profits accrued evenly during the year.

Prepare the appropriation account (on the next page) for the partnership for the year ended 31 March 20X1.

Partnership Appropriation account for the year ended 31 March 20X1

	1 April 20X0 – 30 June 20X0 £	1 July 20X0 – 31 March 20X1 £	Total £
Profit			
Salaries:			
Jane			
Kate			
Lysa			
Interest on capital:			
Jane			
Kate			
Lysa			
Profit available for distribution			

Profit share			
Jane			
Kate			
Lysa			
Total profit distributed			

Task 2.4

This task is about preparing a partnership statement of financial position.

You are preparing the statement of financial position for the Beacon Partnership for the year ended 31 March 20X1. The partners are Yulia and Zoe.

All the necessary year end adjustments have been made, except for the transfer of profit to the current accounts of the partners.

Before sharing profits the balances of the partners' current accounts are:

- Yulia   £950 debit

- Zoe   £450 credit

Each partner is entitled to £5,250 profit share.

(a) **Calculate the balance of each partner's current account after sharing profits. Fill in the answers below.**

Current account balance: Yulia	£
Current account balance: Zoe	£

Note: these balances will need to be transferred into the statement of financial position of the partnership which follows.

You have the following trial balance. All the necessary year end adjustments have been made.

(b) Prepare a statement of financial position for the partnership as at 31 March 20X1. You need to use the partners' current account balances that you have just calculated. Do NOT use brackets, minus signs or dashes.

Beacon Partnership
Trial balance as at 31 March 20X1

		Dr £	Cr £
SCP.	Accruals		690
IS	Administration expenses	20,830	
SFP.	Allowance for doubtful debts		1,400
IS	Allowance for doubtful debts: adjustment	250	
SFP.	Bank	11,750	
SFP	Capital account – Yulia		30,000
SFP.	Capital account – Zoe		22,000
SFP	Cash	220	
SFP.	Closing inventory	17,380	17,380
SFP	Current account – Yulia	950	
SFP.	Current account – Zoe		450
IS	Depreciation charge	4,650	
IS	Disposal of non-current asset		540
SCP	Office equipment at cost	24,400	
SFP.	Office equipment: accumulated depreciation		10,250
IS	Opening inventory	15,140	
IS	Purchases	85,460	
SCP.	Purchases ledger control		11,680
IS	Sales revenue		155,230
SCP	Sales ledger control	35,380	
SFP IS	Value Added Tax		3,110
IS	Wages	36,320	
	Total	252,730	252,730

Beacon Partnership

Statement of financial position as at 31 March 20X1

Non-current (fixed) assets	Cost £	Accumulated depreciation £	Carrying amount (net book value) £
Current assets			
Current liabilities			
Net current assets			
Net assets			
Financed by:	**Yulia**	**Zoe**	**Total**

Accounts preparation 2

Practice assessment 2

Time allowance: 2 hours

- This Assessment is based on a sample assessment provided by the AAT and is reproduced here with their kind permission.

- Each task of the Assessment is to be answered separately.

- The rate of Value Added Tax used is 20%.

Section 1 – Incomplete records

Task 1.1

This task is about finding missing figures in ledger accounts where the records are incomplete.

You are working on the final accounts of a business for the year ended 31 March 20X1. You have the following information:

Day book summaries:	Goods £	VAT £	Total £
Sales	134,000	26,800	160,800
Purchases	90,000	18,000	108,000

Balances as at:	31 March X0 £	31 March X1 £
Trade debtors	15,700	14,300
Trade creditors	9,800	12,450

All sales and purchases are on credit terms

Further information:	Net £	VAT £	Total £
Office expenses	3,600	720	4,320

Office expenses are not included in the purchases day book

Bank summary	**Dr £**		**Cr £**
Balance b/d	9,620	Travel expenses	1,600
Trade debtors	158,320	Office expenses	4,320
Interest received	63	Trade creditors	103,470
		HMRC for VAT	7,315
		Drawings	26,000
		Payroll expenses	11,090
		Balance c/d	14,208
	168,003		168,003

(a)   Using the figures given, prepare the purchases ledger control account for the year ended 31 March 20X1. Show clearly discounts as the balancing figure.

Purchases ledger control account

(b)   Find the closing balance for VAT by preparing the VAT control account for the year ended 31 March 20X1. Use the figures given on the previous page.

Note: The business is not charged VAT on its travel expenses.

VAT control

		Balance b/d	1,800

Task 1.2

This task is about calculating missing balances and the accounting equation.

You are given the following information about a sole trader as at 1 April 20X0:

The value of assets and liabilities were:

■	Fixed assets at net book value	£12,500
■	Trade debtors	£2,450
■	Bank (overdrawn)	£860
■	Trade creditors	£1,380

There were no other assets or liabilities.

(a) Calculate the capital account balance as at 1 April 20X0.

£

(b) On 30 April 20X0, a new computer is purchased on credit. Tick the boxes to show what effect this transaction will have on the balances. You must choose ONE answer for EACH line.

✓

	Debit	Credit	No change
Fixed assets			
Trade debtors			
Trade creditors			
Bank			
Capital			

(c) Which of the following is best described as a current asset? Choose ONE answer.

✓

(a)	An item of stock that will be sold in the next month.	
(b)	A delivery van that will be sold in the next month.	
(c)	A loan that will be paid back to the bank in the next month.	
(d)	A purchase invoice for insurance that will be paid in the next month.	

Section 2 – Final Accounts

Task 2.1

This task is about preparing final accounts for sole traders.

You have the following trial balance for a sole trader known as Onyx Trading. All the necessary year-end adjustments have been made.

(a)   Prepare a profit and loss account for the business for the year ended 31 March 20X1.

Onyx Trading		
Trial balance as at 31 March 20X1		
	Dr	Cr
	£	£
Accruals		1,500
Bank	1,660	
Capital		9,000
Closing stock	17,000	17,000
Depreciation charge	5,100	
Discounts allowed	3,760	
Drawings	12,000	
General expenses	30,845	
Machinery at cost	20,400	
Machinery accumulated depreciation		10,200
Opening stock	18,520	
Prepayments	2,000	
Purchases	110,740	
Purchases ledger control account		14,920
Rent	13,200	
Sales		209,890
Sales ledger control account	18,145	
VAT		4,860
Wages	14,000	
	267,370	267,370

Handwritten annotations in left margin: SP, SP, SP, BoL, IS, IS, SP, IS, SP, SP, IS, SP, IS, SP, IS, IS, SP, SP, IS

Onyx Trading

Profit and loss account for the year ended 31 March 20X1

	£	£
Sales		
Cost of goods sold		
Gross profit		
Less:		
Total expenses		
Net profit		

(b) Indicate where the drawings should be shown in the final accounts. Choose ONE from:

		✓
(a)	As an addition to capital.	
(b)	As a deduction from capital.	
(c)	As an addition to expenses.	
(d)	As a deduction from expenses.	

(c) Identify ONE valid reason for producing a trial balance from:

		✓
(a)	It proves that no errors have been made.	
(b)	It provides a net profit figure.	
(c)	It shows where figures appear in the final accounts.	
(d)	It proves that double entry has taken place.	

Task 2.2

This task is about accounting for partnerships.

You have the following information about a partnership:

The partners are Sam and Terry.

■ Riva was admitted to the partnership on 1 April 20X1 when she introduced £50,000 to the bank account.

■ Profit share, effective until 31 March 20X1:

· Sam   50%

· Terry   50%

■ Profit share, effective from 1 April 20X1:

· Sam   40%

· Terry   40%

· Riva   20%

■ Goodwill was valued at £36,000 on 31 March 20X1.

■ Goodwill is to be introduced into the partners' capital accounts on 31 March and then eliminated on 1 April.

(a) Prepare the capital account for Riva, the new partner, showing clearly the balance carried down as at 1 April 20X1.

Capital account – Riva

		Balance b/d	0

(b) Complete the following sentence by selecting the appropriate phrase in each case:

When a partner retires from a partnership business, the balance on the (**business bank account/partner's capital account/partner's current account**) must be transferred to the (**partner's capital account/partner's current account**).

Task 2.3

This task is about partnership accounts. You have the following information about a partnership business:

■ The financial year ends on 31 March.

■ The partners at the beginning of the year were Asma, Ben and Chris.

■ Asma retired on 30 September 20X0.

■ Partners' annual salaries:

· Asma £20,500

· Ben £25,000

· Chris nil

■ Partners' interest on capital:

· Asma £1,500 per full year

· Ben £1,500 per full year

· Chris £1,500 per full year

■ Profit share, effective until 30 September 20X0:

· Asma 50%

· Ben 25%

· Chris 25%

■ Profit share, effective from 1 October 20X0:

· Ben 60%

· Chris 40%

Net profit for the year ended 31 March 20X1 was £100,000. You can assume that profits accrued evenly during the year.

Variant 1: Prepare the appropriation account for the partnership for the year ended 31 March 20X1.

Partnership Appropriation account for the year ended 31 March 20X1

	1 April X0 – 30 September X0 £	1 October X0 – 31 March X1 £	Total £
Net profit			
Salaries:			
Asma			
Ben			
Chris			
Interest on capital:			
Asma			
Ben			
Chris			
Profit available for distribution			

Profit share			
Asma			
Ben			
Chris			
Total profit distributed			

Variant 2:

You have the following information about a partnership:

- The financial year ends on 31 March.
- The partners are Asma, Ben and Chris.
- Partners' annual salaries:
  - Asma £8,250
  - Ben £18,000
  - Chris nil
- Partners' capital account balances as at 31 March 20X1:
  - Asma £25,000
  - Ben £50,000
  - Chris £50,000

Interest on capital is charged at 3% per annum on the capital account balance at the end of the financial year.

- The partners share the remaining profit of £40000 as follows:
  - Asma 20%
  - Ben 50%
  - Chris 30%
- Partners' drawings for the year:
  - Asma £16,000
  - Ben £40,000
  - Chris £13,000

Prepare the current accounts for the partners for the year ended 31 March 20X1. Show clearly the balances carried down. You MUST enter zeros where appropriate in order to obtain full marks. Do NOT use brackets, minus signs or dashes.

Current accounts

	Asma £	Ben £	Chris £		Asma £	Ben £	Chris £
Balance b/d	400	0	0	Balance b/d	0	1,500	0

Task 2.4 – Partnership balance sheet

This task is about preparing a partnership balance sheet.

You are preparing the balance sheet for the Onyx partnership for the year ended 31 March 20X1. The partners are Jon and Pat.

All the necessary year end adjustments have been made, except for the transfer of profit to the current accounts of the partners.

Before sharing profits the balances of the partners' current accounts are:

- Jon   £250 credit
- Pat   £356 credit

Each partner is entitled to £5,000 profit share.

(a)   Calculate the balance of each partner's current account after sharing profits. Fill in the answers below.

Current account balance: Jon £
Current account balance: Pat £

Note: these balances will need to be transferred into the balance sheet of the partnership which follows.

You have the following trial balance. All the necessary year-end adjustments have been made.

(b)   Prepare a balance sheet for the partnership as at 31 March 20X1. You need to use the partners' current account balances that you have just calculated. Do NOT use brackets, minus signs or dashes.

Onyx Partnership
Trial balance as at 31 March 20X1

	Dr £	Cr £
Accruals		850
Administration expenses	38,890	
Bank	3,936	
Capital – Jon		30,000
Capital – Pat		25,000
Cash	350	
Closing stock	22,570	22,570
Current account – Jon		250
Current account – Pat		356
Depreciation charge	4,185	
Disposal of fixed asset	800	
Motor vehicles at cost	37,500	
Motor vehicles accumulated depreciation		16,125
Opening stock	20,475	
Allowance for doubtful debts		900
Change in allowance for doubtful debts	85	
Purchases	85,724	
Purchases ledger control account		24,600
Sales		162,324
Sales ledger control account	47,000	
Selling expenses	24,735	
VAT		3,275
Total	286,250	286,250

Onyx Partnership

Balance sheet as at 31 March 20X1

Fixed assets	Cost £	Depreciation £	Net Book Value £
Current assets			
Current liabilities			
Net current assets			
Net assets			

Financed by:	Jon	Pat	Total

Accounts preparation 2

Practice assessment 3

Time allowance: 2 hours

- Each task of the Assessment is to be answered separately.
- The rate of Value Added Tax used is 20%.

Section 1: Tasks and Questions

Task 1.1

This task is about finding missing figures in the general ledger accounts where the records are incomplete.

You are working on the accounts of a sole trader for the year ended 31 March 20X6.

The business is not registered for VAT.

You have the following information:

Receipts and payments recorded in the bank account include:

	£
Amounts from credit customers	67,031
Amounts to credit suppliers	27,846
Drawings	12,500
Office expenses	19,361
Bank interest paid	247

Balance at:	31 March 20X5	31 March 20X6
	£	£
Trade receivables	8,216	9.047
Trade payables	4,367	4,498
Closing inventory	4,221	4,864
Bank	3,219 credit	1,246 debit

You are also told that:

• All sales are on credit terms

• Sales totalled £68,422 for the year

(a)   **Find the credit purchases figure by preparing the purchases ledger control account for the year ended 31 March 20X6.**

Select your entries for the details column from the following list:

Allowance for doubtful debts, Allowance for doubtful debts adjustment, Balance b/d, Balance c/d, Bank, Bank interest paid, Capital, Cash purchases, Cash sales, Credit purchases, Credit sales, Drawings, Inventory – opening, Inventory – closing, Irrecoverable debts, Office expenses, Purchases ledger control, Sales ledger control.

Purchases ledger control account

	£		£

During the year, a customer was declared bankrupt. The amount has been written off in full.

(b) **Find the amount written off by preparing the sales ledger control account for the year ended 31 March 20X6.**

Sales ledger control account

	£		£

(c) **Find the cash purchases by preparing a summarised bank account for the year ended 31 March 20X6.**

Bank

	£		£
		Balance b/d	3,219
		Balance c/d	1,246

Task 1.2

This task is about missing figures and the accounting equation.

You have the following information about events on 1 April 20X5.

- A sole trader started business.

- The business was not registered for VAT.

- The sole trader transferred £20,000 of her own money into the business bank account.

- £8,000 was paid from this account for a delivery van.

- Goods for resale by the business costing £1,200 were purchased using the trader's personal bank account.

(a)   **Complete the capital account as at 1 April 20X5, showing clearly the balance carried down.**

Select your entries for the details column from the following list:

Balance b/d, Balance c/d, Bank, Delivery van at cost, Drawings, Purchases, Purchases ledger control, Sales, Sales ledger control, Suspense.

Capital

	£		£
		Balance b/d	0

The following day, the sole trader bought furniture for use in the office at a cost of £1,500. This was paid for from the business bank account and the transaction was entered in the records.

(b)   **Tick the appropriate boxes to show how this transaction affects the elements of the accounting equation below.**

You must choose ONE answer for EACH row.

✓

	Increase	Decrease	No change
Assets			
Liabilities			
Capital			

At the end of the financial year on 31 March 20X6, you have the following further information:

• Total sales were £80,000.

• Total purchases were £67,340.

• A mark-up of 25% on cost was used throughout the year.

(c)   Calculate the value of the cost of goods sold for the year ended 31 March 20X6.

£

(d)   Calculate the value of inventory as at 31 March 20X6.

£

You are given the following information about another sole trader.

• The cash book shows a credit balance of £7,290.

• The bank statement on the same date shows that the business has a debit balance of £5,360.

(e)   Which ONE of the following could explain this difference?

✓

Bank charges on the bank statement have not been entered in the cash book.	
Cheques to suppliers sent out at the end of the month have not yet cleared.	
A BACS receipt from a trade receivable has been posted to the bank account twice.	

Section 2

Task 2.1

This task is about preparing financial statements for sole traders.

You have the following trial balance for a sole trader known as Hanslo Trading. All the necessary year end adjustments have been made.

The following are accounting policies used by Hanslo:

- Sales revenue should include sales returns, if any.
- Purchases should include purchases returns and carriage inwards, if any.

(a)   Calculate the sales revenue figure to be included in the income statement for Hanslo.

£

(b)   Calculate the purchases figure to be included in the income statement for Hanslo.

£

(c)   **Prepare an income statement (on the next page) for Hanslo Trading for the year ended 31 March 20X6. If necessary, use a minus sign to indicate a loss for the year.**

Hanslo Trading Trial balance as at 31 March 20X6	Dr £	Cr £
Accruals		740
Bank	4,850	
Capital		65,000
Carriage inwards	1,430	
Carriage outwards	2,790	
Cash	220	
Closing inventory	11,340	11,340
Depreciation charges	4,520	
Disposal of non-current assets		990
Drawings	16,500	
General expenses	23,920	
Opening inventory	9,760	
Prepayments	1,310	
Purchases	47,860	
Purchases ledger control		7,530
Sales		125,860
Sales ledger control	18,170	
Sales returns	2,160	
VAT		2,710
Vehicles at cost	35,000	
Vehicles accumulated depreciation		14,710
Wages	49,050	
Total	228,880	228,880

Hanslo Trading
Income statement for the year ended 31 March 20X6

	£	£
Sales revenue		
Cost of goods sold		
Gross profit		
Other income:		
Less:		
Total expenses		
Profit/loss for the year		

(d)   **Identify the meaning of a debit balance for disposal of non-current assets in a trial balance. Tick ONE from:**

	✓
The business has made a profit on disposal.	
The business has made a loss on disposal.	
The asset has been over-depreciated.	
The asset has been part-exchanged on disposal.	

(e)   **"Financial information gives a complete and faithful representation."**

Identify the objective of financial information that best fits with the above statement.

Tick ONE from:

	✓
Relevance	
Reliability	
Comparability	
Ease of understanding	

Task 2.2

This task is about accounting for partnerships.

You have the following information about a partnership:

Hal and Ian have been the owners of a partnership business for many years sharing profits and losses in the ratio 2:1, with Hal receiving the larger share.

On 1 October 20X5, the partnership agreement was changed so that Hal and Ian will share profits and losses in the ratio 3:2, with Hal receiving the larger share.

Goodwill was valued at £60,000 at this date and has already been introduced into the partnership accounting records. It now needs to be eliminated.

(a) **Show the entries required to eliminate the goodwill from the partnership accounting records on 1 October 20X5.**

Select you entries for the 'Account name' column from the following list:

Balance b/d, Balance c/d, Bank, Capital – Hal, Capital – Ian, Current – Hal, Current – Ian, Goodwill.

Account name	Amount £	Debit	Credit

(b) **Complete the following statements regarding Hal's position in the partnership at the end of the day on 1 October 20X5 by selecting the appropriate phrase.**

Hal's share of the profits and losses in the partnership has

INCREASED / DECREASED / STAYED THE SAME

after the change in the partnership agreement.

Hal's capital account balance has

INCREASED / DECREASED / STAYED THE SAME

after the change in the partnership agreement.

(c) **Identify whether the following statements are true or false by putting a tick in the relevant column of the table below.**

Statement	True ✔	False ✔
When a new partner is admitted to a partnership business, existing partners pay a premium to welcome the new partner.		
When a partner retires from a partnership business, the balance of his or her capital and current accounts is paid to the partner from the partnership bank account (subject to sufficient funds being available).		

Task 2.3

This task is about partnership accounts.

You have the following information about a partnership business:

- The financial year ends on 31 March.

- The partners are Amy, Bob and Caz.

- Interest on capital is allowed at 5.0% per annum on the capital account balances at the end of the financial year.

- Interest on drawings is charges to the partners and is shown in the table below.

	Amy	Bob	Caz
	£	£	£
Annual salaries	10,000	12,500	nil
Capital account balances, 31 March 20X5	60,000	35,000	26,000
Capital account balances, 31 March 20X6	65,000	35,000	28,000
Drawings for the year	30,000	28,500	8,500
Interest on drawings for the year	300	285	85

- The profit for distribution to the partners after appropriations is £43,000.

- Profits are shared in the following percentages: Amy 50%, Bob 30%, Caz 20%.

Prepare the current accounts for the partners for the year ended 31 March 20X6. Show clearly the balances carried down.

You MUST enter zeros where appropriate in order to obtain full marks.

Do NOT use brackets, minus signs or dashes.

Select your entries for the details column from the following list:

Balance b/d, Balance c/d, Bank, Capital – Amy, Capital – Bob, Capital – Caz, Current – Amy, Current – Bob, Current – Caz, Drawings, Goodwill, Interest on capital, Interest on drawings, Salaries, Share of loss, Share of profit.

Current accounts

Details	Amy £	Bob £	Caz £	Details	Amy £	Bob £	Caz £
Balance b/d			210	Balance b/d	2,320	830	

Task 2.4

This task is about preparing a partnership statement of financial position.

You are preparing the statement of financial position for the Blenheim partnership for the year ended 31 March 20X6.

The partners are Yan and Zeb.

You have the final trial balance on the opposite page. All the necessary year end adjustments have been made, except for the transfer of £36,000 profit to the current accounts of the partners. Partners share profits and losses in the ratio 2:3, with Zeb taking the larger share.

(a)   Calculate the balance of each partner's current account after sharing profits. Indicate whether these balances are **DEBIT** or **CREDIT**.

Current account : Yan £	DEBIT/CREDIT
Current account : Zeb £	DEBIT/CREDIT

(b)   **Prepare a statement of financial position for the partnership as at 31 March 20X6. You need to use the partners' current account balances that you have just calculated in (a).**

Do NOT use brackets, minus signs or dashes.

Blenheim Partnership
Trial balance as at 31 March 20X6

	Dr £	Cr £
Accruals		550
Administration expenses	39,179	
Bank	10,875	
Capital account – Yan		35,000
Capital account – Zeb		50,000
Cash	240	
Closing inventory	17,830	17,830
Current account – Yan	820	
Current account – Zeb		2,090
Depreciation charges	5,400	
Discounts received		1,210
Disposal of non-current asset	455	
Irrecoverable debts	394	
Machinery at cost	87,500	
Machinery accumulated depreciation		22,840
Opening inventory	16,380	
Prepayments	725	
Purchases	261,340	
Purchases ledger control		33,025
Sales		390,860
Sales returns	2,390	
Sales ledger control	64,055	
Travel expenses	14,497	
VAT		2,540
Wages	33,865	
Total	555,945	555,945

Blenheim Partnership

Statement of financial position as at 31 March 20X6

Non-current (fixed) assets	Cost £	Accumulated depreciation £	Carrying amount £
Current assets			
Total current assets			
Current liabilities			
Total current liabilities			
Net current assets			
Net assets			
Financed by:	**Yan**	**Zeb**	**Total**

Practice assessment answers

1 Accounts preparation 2
Practice assessment – answers

Section 1

Task 1.1

(a)   Sales ledger control account

Balance b/d	18,275	Sales returns day book	2,880
Sales day book	160,800	Bank	152,490
		Discounts allowed	230
		Balance c/d	23,475
	179,075		179,075

(b)   Purchases ledger control account

Purchases returns day book	1,920	Balance b/d	10,365
Bank	92,845	Purchases day book	98,400
Discounts received	550		
Balance c/d	13,450		
	108,765		108,765

(c)   VAT control account

Sales returns day book	480	Balance b/d	2,140
Purchases day book	16,400	Sales day book	26,800
Office expenses	4,120	Purchases returns day book	320
Bank	5,245		
Balance c/d	3,015		
	29,260		29,260

Task 1.2

(a)

£27,330

(b)

£52,090

(c)

An intangible non-current asset which does not have material substance.	✔

Section 2

Task 2.1

(a)

Tairo Trading Income statement for the year ended 31 March 20X1		
	£	£
Sales revenue		160,830
Opening inventory	6,290	
Purchases	93,760	
Closing inventory	(8,350)	
Cost of sales		91,700
Gross profit		69,130
Less expenses:		
Depreciation charge	6,240	
Discounts allowed	350	
General expenses	13,860	
Rent and rates	10,390	
Wages	28,450	
Total expenses		59,290
Profit for the year		9,840

(b)

As a current asset	✓

(c)

Statement	Objective
Financial information that is useful to users of the financial statements.	relevance
Financial information that can be depended upon by users.	reliability
Financial statements that can be compared with those from previous years.	comparability
Users of financial statements can understand the information given.	ease of understanding

Task 2.2

(a)   Capital account – Kay

	£		£
		Balance b/d	48,500
Loan	25,000	Goodwill	12,000
Bank	35,500		
	60,500		60,500

(b)

Statement	True ✔	False ✔
All partnership agreements state that profits and losses must be shared equally between the partners.		✔
A partnership agreement will state the salaries to be paid to employees.		✔
A partnership agreement may state that interest is to be allowed on partners' capitals, and at what rate.	✔	
A partnership agreement may state that interest is to be charged on partners' drawings, and at what rate.	✔	

Task 2.3

Partnership Appropriation account for the year ended 31 March 20X1

	1 April 20X0 – 30 June 20X0 £	1 July 20X0 – 31 March 20X1 £	Total £
Profit	17,000	51,000	68,000
Salaries:			
Jane	5,000	15,000	20,000
Kate	6,000	18,000	24,000
Lysa	–	–	–
Interest on capital:			
Jane	300	900	1,200
Kate	450	1,350	1,800
Lysa	–	300	300
Profit available for distribution	5,250	15,450	20,700

Profit share			
Jane	3,150	7,725	10,875
Kate	2,100	4,635	6,735
Lysa	–	3,090	3,090
Total profit distributed	5,250	15,450	20,700

Task 2.4

(a)

Current account balance: Yulia	£4,300
Current account balance: Zoe	£5,700

(b) **Beacon Partnership**
Statement of financial position as at 31 March 20X1

Non-current (fixed) assets	Cost £	Accumulated depreciation £	Carrying amount (net book value) £
Office equipment	24,400	10,250	14,150
Current assets			
Inventory		17,380	
Trade receivables		*33,980	
Bank		11,750	
Cash		220	
		63,330	
Current liabilities			
Trade payables	11,680		
Value Added Tax	3,110		
Accruals	690		
		15,480	
Net current assets			47,850
Net assets			62,000

Financed by:	Yulia	Zoe	Total
Capital accounts	30,000	22,000	52,000
Current accounts	4,300	5,700	10,000
	34,300	27,700	62,000

* sales ledger control £35,380 minus allowance for doubtful debts £1,400

Accounts Preparation 2
Answers to Assessment 2

Section 1

Task 1.1

(a) **Purchases ledger control account**

Bank	103,470	Balance b/d	9,800
Discounts received	1,880	Purchases day book	108,000
Balance c/d	12,450		
	117,800		117,800

(b) **VAT Control**

Purchases day book	18,000	Balance b/d	1,800
Office expenses	720	Sales day book	26,800
Bank	7,315		
Balance c/d	2,565		
	28,600		28,600

Task 1.2

(a) £12,710

(b)

	Debit	Credit	No change
Fixed assets	✓		
Trade debtors			✓
Trade creditors		✓	
Bank			✓
Capital			✓

(c) (a) An item of stock that will be sold in the next month.

Section 2

Task 2.1

(a)

Onyx Trading		
Profit and loss account for the year ended 31 March 20X1		
	£	£
Sales		209,890
Opening stock	18,520	
Purchases	110,740	
Closing stock	(17,000)	
Cost of goods sold		112,260
Gross profit		97,630
Less:		
Depreciation charge	5,100	
Discounts allowed	3,760	
General expenses	30,845	
Rent	13,200	
Wages	14,000	
Total expenses		66,905
Net profit		30,725

(b) (b) As a deduction from capital.

(c) (d) It proves that double entry has taken place.

Task 2.2

(a) **Capital account - Riva**

Goodwill	7,200	Balance b/d	0
Balance c/d	42,800	Bank	50,000
	50,000		50,000

(b) When a partner retires from a partnership business, the balance on the **partner's current account** must be transferred to the **partner's capital account**.

Task 2.3

Variant 1:

Partnership Appropriation account for the year ended 31 March 20X1

	1 April X0 – 30 September X0	1 October X0 – 31 March X1	Total
	£	£	£
Net profit	50,000	50,000	100,000
Salaries:			
Asma	10,250	0	10,250
Ben	12,500	12,500	25,000
Chris	0	0	0
Interest on capital:			
Asma	750	0	750
Ben	750	750	1,500
Chris	750	750	1,500
Profit available for distribution	25,000	36,000	61,000

Profit share:			
Asma	12,500	0	12,500
Ben	6,250	21,600	27,850
Chris	6,250	14,400	20,650
Total profit distributed	25,000	36,000	61,000

Variant 2:

Current accounts

	Asma £	Ben £	Chris £		Asma £	Ben £	Chris £
Balance b/d	400	0	0	Balance b/d	0	1,500	0
Drawings	16,000	40,000	13,000	Salaries	8,250	18,000	0
Balance c/d	600	1,000	500	Interest on capital	750	1,500	1,500
				Profit share	8,000	20,000	12,000
	17,000	41,000	13,500		17,000	41,000	13,500

Task 2.4

(a)   Jon   £5,250

       Pat   £5,356

(b)

Onyx Partnership

Balance sheet as at 31 March 20X1

Fixed assets	Cost	Depreciation	Net Book Value
	£	£	£
Motor vehicles at cost	37,500	16,125	21,375
Current assets			
Stock		22,570	
Trade debtors		46,100	
Bank		3,936	
Cash		350	
		72,956	
Current liabilities			
Trade creditors	24,600		
VAT	3,275		
Accruals	850		
		28,725	
Net current assets			44,231
Net assets			65,606
Financed by:	**Jon**	**Pat**	**Total**
Capital accounts	30,000	25,000	55,000
Current accounts	5,250	5,356	10,606
	35,250	30,356	65,606

Accounts Preparation 2
Answers to Assessment 3

Section 1: Tasks and Questions

Task 1.1

(a) **Purchase ledger control account**

	£		£
Bank	27,846	Balance b/d	4,367
Balance c/d	4,498	Credit purchases	27,977
	32,344		32,344

(b) **Sales ledger control account**

	£		£
Balance b/d	8,216	Bank	67,031
Credit sales	68,422	Irrecoverable debts	560
		Balance c/d	9,047
	76,638		76,638

(c) **Bank**

	£		£
Sales ledger control	67,031	Balance b/d	3,219
		Purchases ledger control	27,846
		Drawings	12,500
		Office expenses	19,361
		Bank interest paid	247
		Cash purchases	2,612
		Balance c/d	1,246
	67,031		67,031

Task 1.2

(a)

Capital

	£		£
Balance c/d	21,200	Balance b/d	0
		Bank	20,000
		Purchases	1,200
	21,200		21,200

(b)

	Increase	Decrease	No change
Assets			✓
Liabilities			✓
Capital			✓

(c) **£64,000** [calculation: (£80,000 ÷ 125) x 100]

(d) **£3,340** [calculation: £67,340 − £64,000]

(e) Cheques to suppliers sent out at the end of the month have not yet cleared.

Section 2

Task 2.1

(a)   **£123,700** [ie £125,860 − £2,160]

(b)   **£49,290** [ie £47,860 + £1,430]

(c)

Hanslo Trading Income statement for the year ended 31 March 20X6	£	£
Sales revenue		123,700
Opening inventory	9,760	
Purchases	49,290	
Closing inventory	−11,340	
Cost of goods sold	47,710	
Gross profit		75,990
Other income:		
Disposal of non-current assets		990
Less		
Carriage outwards	2,790	
Depreciation charges	4,520	
General expenses	23,920	
Wages	49,050	
Total expenses		80,280
Profit/loss for the year		−3,300

(d)   The business has made a loss on disposal.

(e)   Reliability

Task 2.2

(a)

Account name	Amount £	Debit	Credit
Goodwill	60,000		✓
Capital – Hal	36,000	✓	
Capital – Ian	24,000	✓	

(b) Hal's share of the profits and losses in the partnership has DECREASED after the change in the partnership agreement.

Hal's capital account balance has INCREASED after the change in the partnership agreement.

(c)

Statement	True ✓	False ✓
When a new partner is admitted to a partnership business, existing partners pay a premium to welcome the new partner.		✓
When a partner retires from a partnership business, the balance of his or her capital and current accounts is paid to the partner from the partnership bank account (subject to sufficient funds being available).	✓	

Task 2.3

Current accounts

Details	Amy £	Bob £	Caz £	Details	Amy £	Bob £	Caz £
Balance b/d			210	Balance b/d	2,320	830	
Drawings	30,000	28,500	8,500	Salaries	10,000	12,500	0
Interest on drawings	300	285	85	Interest on capital	3,250	1,750	1,400
Balance c/d	6,770		1,205	Share of profit	21,500	12,900	8,600
				Balance c/d		805	
	37,070	28,785	10,000		37,070	28,785	10,000

Task 2.4

(a)

Current account : Yan £13,580	CREDIT
Current account : Zeb £23,690	CREDIT

(b)　　　　　　**Blenheim Partnership**

Statement of financial position as at 31 March 20X6

Non-current (fixed) assets	Cost £	Accumulated depreciation £	Carrying amount (net book value) £
Machinery	87,500	22,840	64,660
Current assets			
Inventory		17,830	
Trade receivables		64,055	
Cash		240	
Prepayments		725	
Bank		10,875	
Total current assets		93,725	
Current liabilities			
Trade payables	33,025		
VAT	2,540		
Accruals	550		
Total current liabilities		36,115	
Net current assets			57,610
Net assets			**122,270**
Financed by:	**Yan**	**Zeb**	**Total**
Capital accounts	35,000	50,000	85,000
Current accounts	13,580	23,690	37,270
	48,580	73,690	**122,270**

for your notes

for your notes

for your notes

for your notes